Usborne First Activities

Animal Fun

Fiona Watt

Illustrated by Katie Lovell

Photographs by Howard Allman

Digital manipulation by Nick Wakeford

Painted lion

For a lioness, don't paint the mane in step 3.

Let the paint dry again.

1. Paint a big yellow oval for a lion's body on some paper.

2. Then, paint four short legs at the bottom. Let it dry.

3. Dip a dry brush into orange paint. Go around and around for a mane.

4. Paint a yellow oval for the face. Then, add two little ears.

5. Paint an orange nose and a shape for the end of the lion's tail.

6. When the paint is dry, use pencils to draw a tail, eyes, a mouth and claws.

Collage crocodile

1. Paint a piece of thick paper and let it dry.

You could paint a river for your crocodiles to swim in.

2. Draw a shape for a body, and two little feet, on the back of the paper.

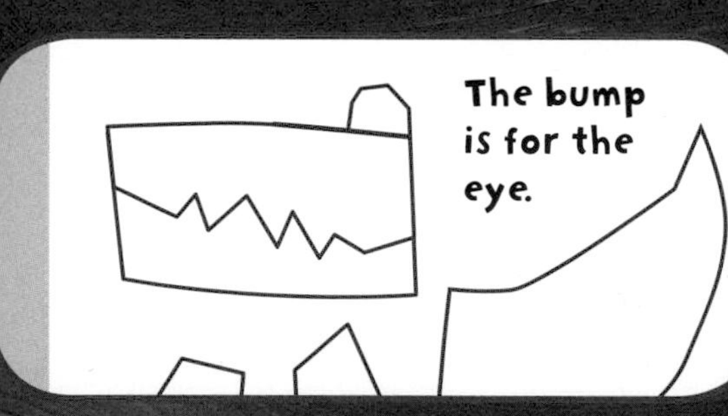

3. Draw a rectangular head. Add a bump on top and zigzag teeth.

4. Cut out all the shapes. Then, lay them on another piece of paper.

5. Glue the body down, then add the other shapes. Draw an eye and a nostril.

Printed parrot

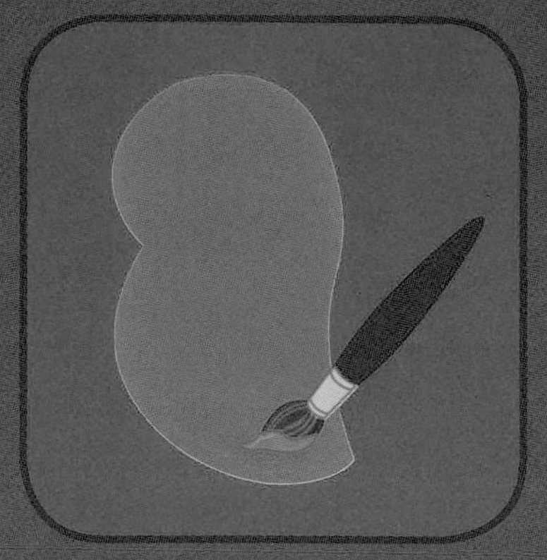

1. Paint a shape for a parrot's body on a piece of thick paper using blue paint. Then, let it dry.

2. Paint feet, a beak and a pink spot on the cheek. Draw a dot for an eye.

3. Paint three red feathers for the parrot's tail. Add a curly feather on the head, too.

4. Spread dark blue paint on an old plate. Press your hand into it, then print a wing.

5. Press your hand into the paint again and print another wing.

You could paint a branch for your parrot to perch on.

Printed giraffe

1. Paint a small rectangle for a body. Add a very long neck.

2. Paint a head, ears and four short legs with a thin brush.

3. Paint an orange nose. Add brown hooves, horns and the end of the tail.

4. Spread orange paint on an old plate. Cut a small square of sponge.

5. Dip the sponge in the paint and print shapes on the body and neck.

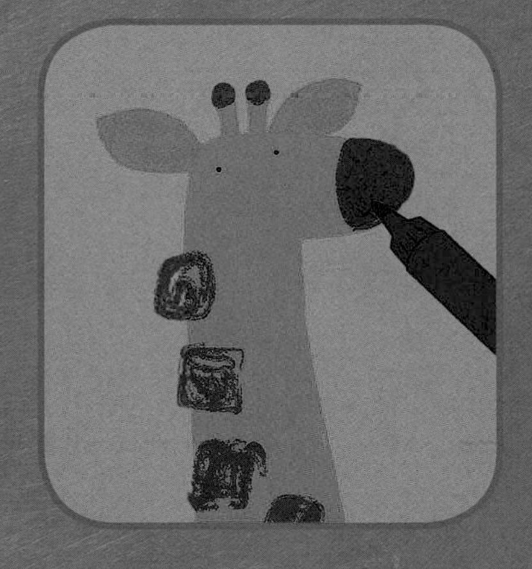

6. When the paint is dry, draw eyes, a nostril and a mouth.

Stand-up elephant

Don't cut along the fold.

Tie a knot in the tail.

1. Fold a piece of thick paper in half. Draw a body against the fold. Add a trunk, too.

2. Cut around the elephant carefully. Then, open it out and lay it flat.

3. Tape on pieces of thread for a tail. Then, spread glue on the end of the trunk.

You could make an elephant from patterned paper.

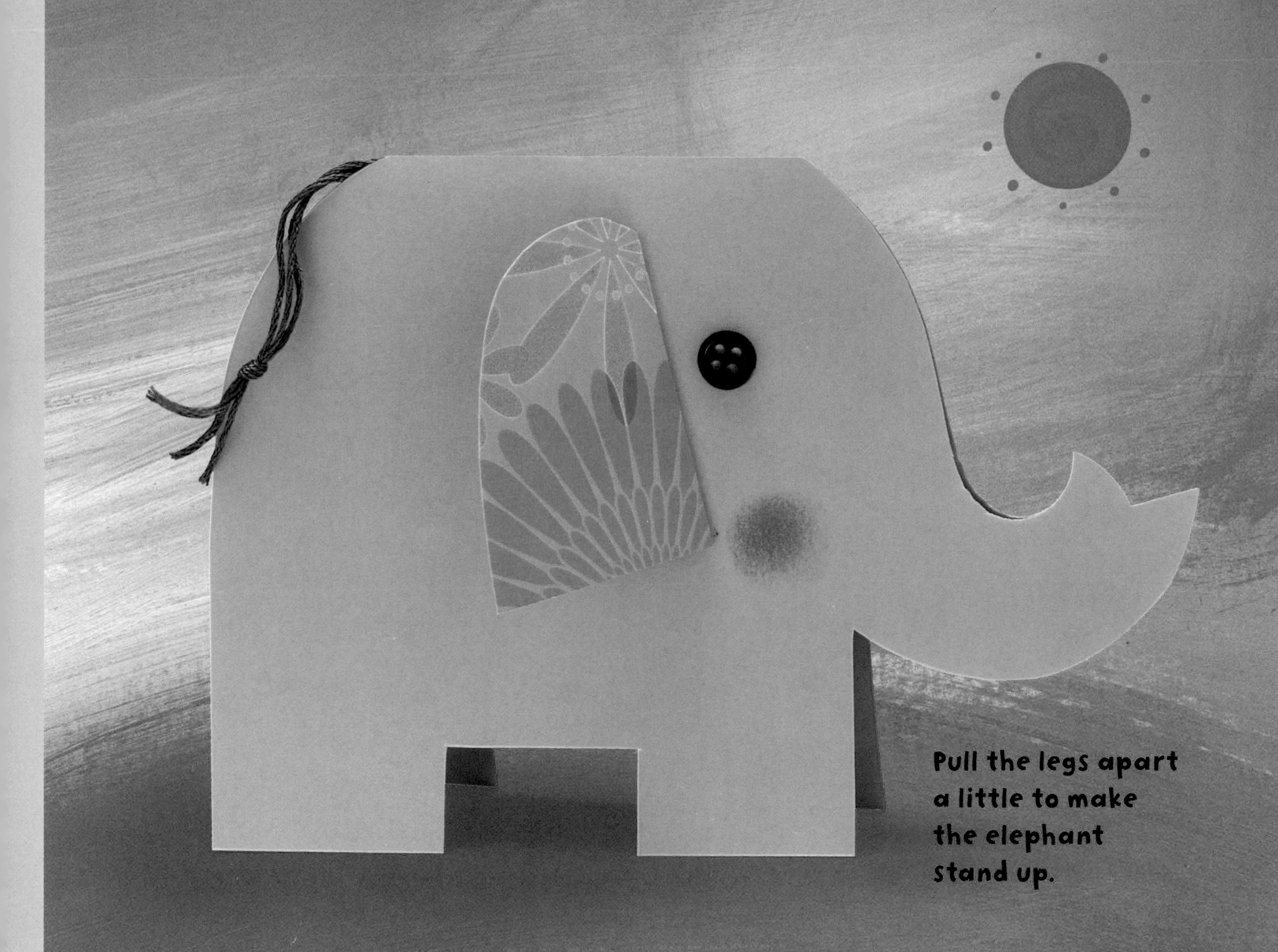

Pull the legs apart a little to make the elephant stand up.

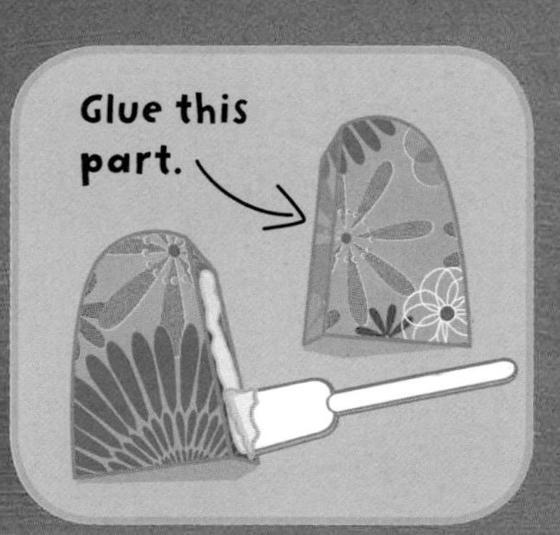

4. Fold the elephant in half again, then press the ends of the trunk together.

5. Cut two ears from patterned paper. Fold the side of each ear and glue it.

6. Glue the ears on either side of the body. Then, glue on old buttons for eyes.

Spotted leopard

1. Dip a finger into yellow paint. Fingerpaint a body.

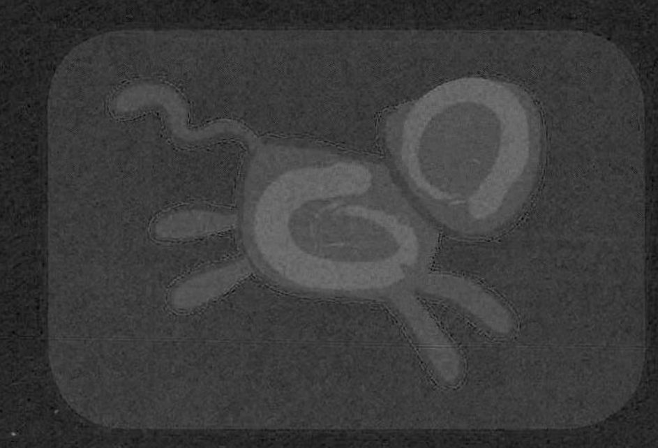

2. Fingerpaint a head and four legs. Add a long tail, too.

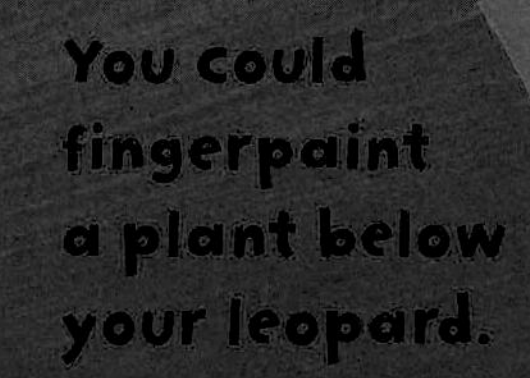

You could fingerpaint a plant below your leopard.

Leave the paint to dry.

3. Fingerprint two yellow dots for ears. Add a brown dot for a nose.

4. Print orange spots all over the leopard. Then, print little brown dots on top.

6. Use pens to draw eyes, a mouth, whiskers and claws.

Striped zebra

Make some of the lines thick and others thin.

1. Paint black stripes on a piece of thick white paper. Let the paint dry.

2. Cut a rectangle for a body from the striped paper. Then, glue it onto some paper.

3. Cut a shape for a neck and one for a head. Glue them onto the body.

4. Cut out ears, legs and a little tail, and glue them on, too.

5. Cut a shape for a nose from pink paper and glue it onto the head.

6. Use pencils to draw a face. Add lines for a hairy mane and tail.

You could cut out grass from bright, striped paper.

Fuzzy monkeys

Use pencils to draw vines for your monkey to hang from.

You could cut out leaves from green felt and glue them around your monkey.

Glue the pieces like this.

1. Cut a head and a small body from felt and glue them onto some paper.

2. Cut out an oval for the face and two little ears from paler felt.

3. Glue the face onto the head. Then, glue the ears on either side.

If you don't have felt, you could make a monkey from paper.

4. Use a crayon to draw curving arms and legs. Add fingers and feet.

5. Draw eyes and a mouth. Then, add pink nostrils and cheeks.

6. Bend a fuzzy pipe cleaner to make a tail. Glue it onto the paper.

Happy hippo

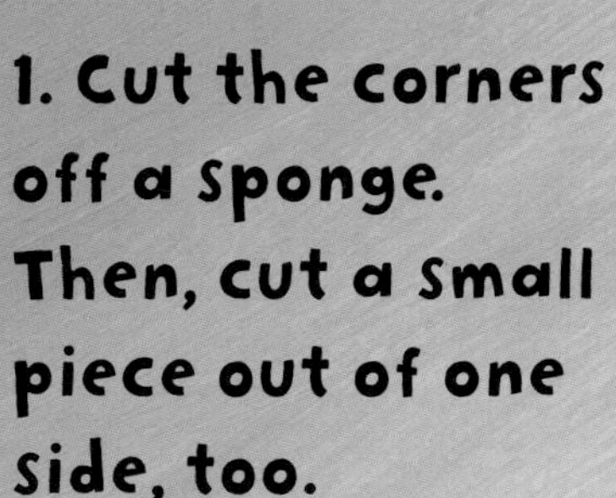

1. Cut the corners off a sponge. Then, cut a small piece out of one side, too.

2. Dip the sponge into some paint and press it onto some paper for the hippo's body.

3. Dip the sponge into the paint again and use it to print a head, like this.

4. Cut a small rectangle for the legs from another sponge. Dip it into the paint.

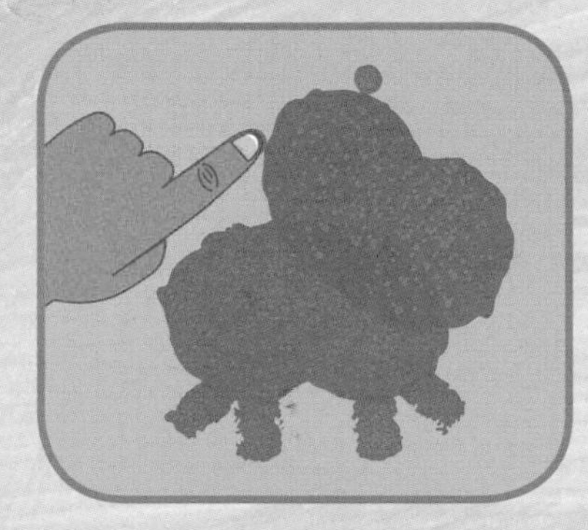

5. Print four legs. Then, use your finger to print two little ears. Leave it to dry.

6. Use pens to draw eyes, nostrils and a mouth. Add square teeth with a white pencil.

You could paint a river and print a hippo on top when the paint is dry.

For a swimming hippo, don't print the legs in step 5.

Hairy bear

1. Mix thick brown paint with lots of white glue in an old container.

Paint a light brown snout, too.

2. Paint an oval for a body. Then, add a head, tail and ears.

3. Paint three legs (the fourth one is hidden behind the bear's body).

You could cut fish from foil and glue them onto your picture.

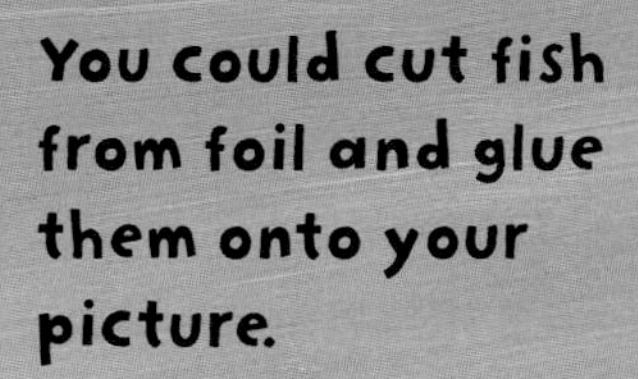

Use the other end of your paintbrush.

4. While the paint is still wet, scratch lots of little lines.

5. When the paint is dry, draw eyes, a nose, a mouth and little brown claws.

You could paint a bear on a rock in a river.

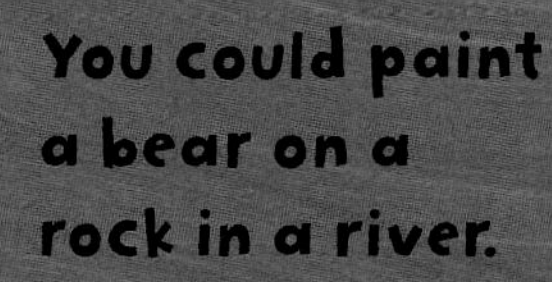

Paper penguin

You could draw a fish on blue paper.

1. Fold a piece of thick black paper in half. Draw a shape for a body.

2. Draw a line at the top for the penguin's beak, like this.

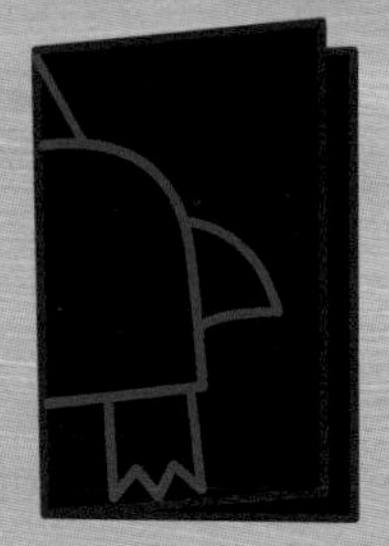

3. Draw a wing halfway down. Add a flipper below, like this.

4. Keeping the paper folded, carefully cut around the shape.

5. Open out the paper and lay it flat. Use pencils to draw two eyes.

6. Draw a line for the tummy, then fill it in. Fill in the flippers, too.

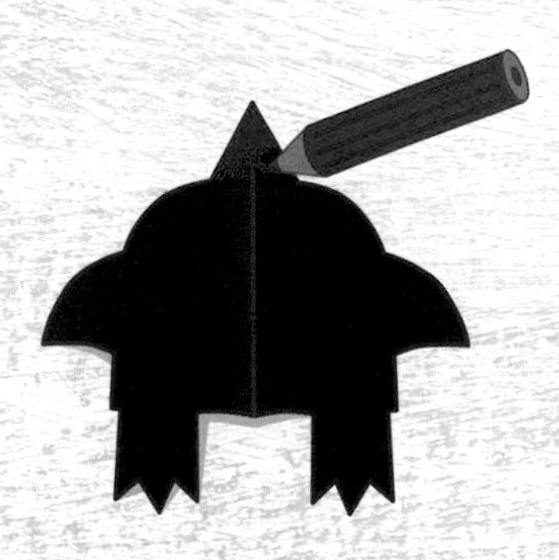

7. Turn the shape over and use an orange pencil to fill in the beak.

8. Fold the beak down and the flippers up. Fold the wings forward.

9. Crease the middle fold again and stand up your penguin.

Wriggly Snakes

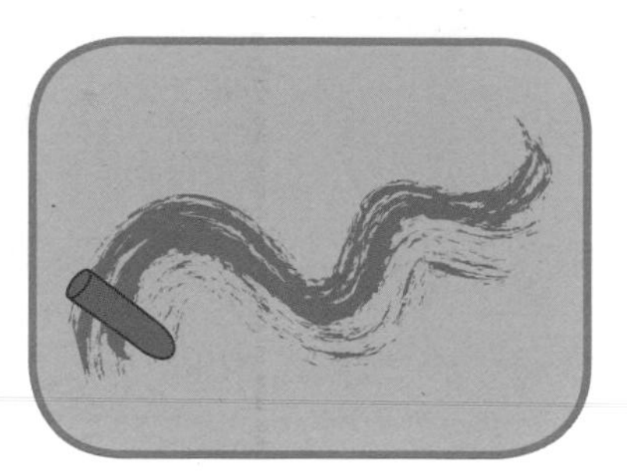

1. Using the side of a piece of chalk, draw a wavy line. Draw a point at one end.

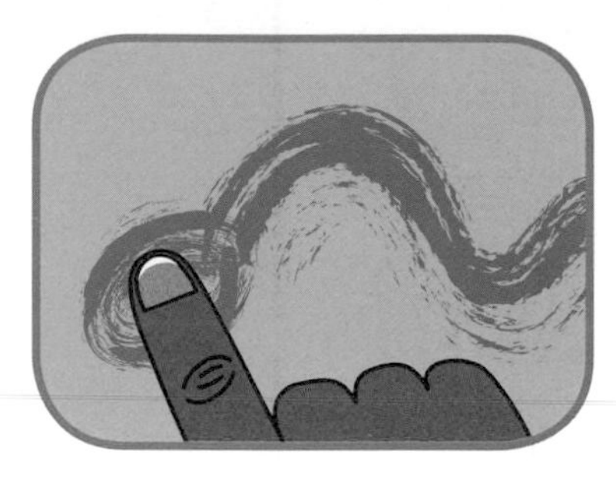

2. Draw an oval head at the flat end. Then, smudge the snake a little with a finger.

3. Draw patterns on the body. Add dots for eyes and two lines for a forked tongue.